I SAW A SHIP A-SAILING

PICTURES BY JANINA DOMANSKA

THE MACMILLAN COMPANY / NEW YORK, NEW

1 2 3 4 5 6 7 8 9 10

The art was done in black pen and ink with overlays for the red, blue and yellow plates.
The typeface is Photo Typositor Abbott Old Style.

 to Anna with love

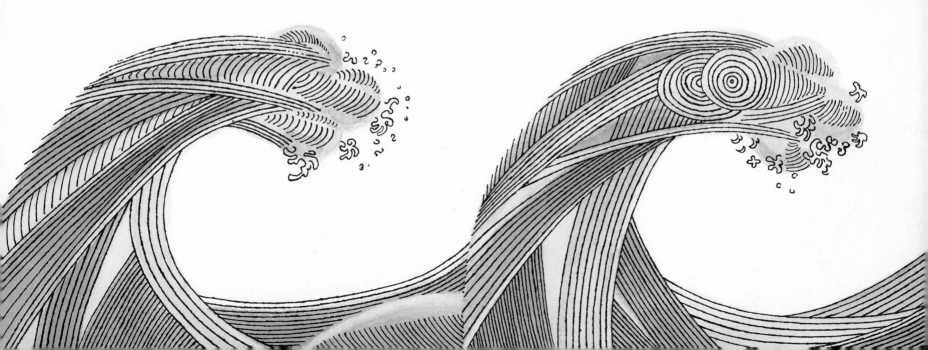

I saw a ship a-sailing,

A-sailing on the sea,

And it was full of pretty things

For you and for me.

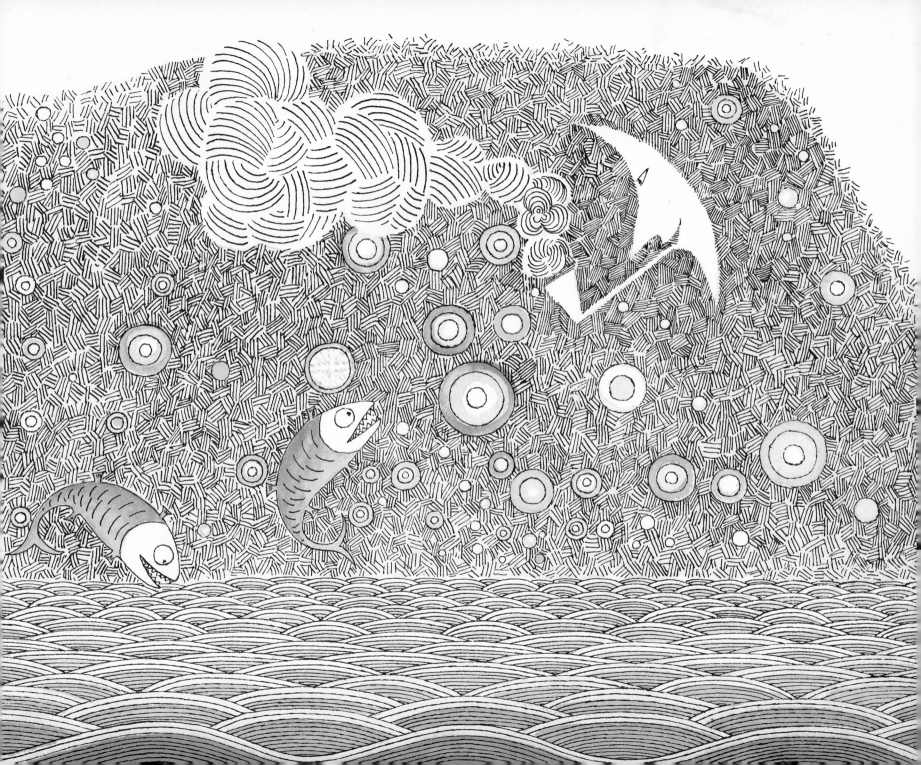

There were sweetmeats in the cabin,

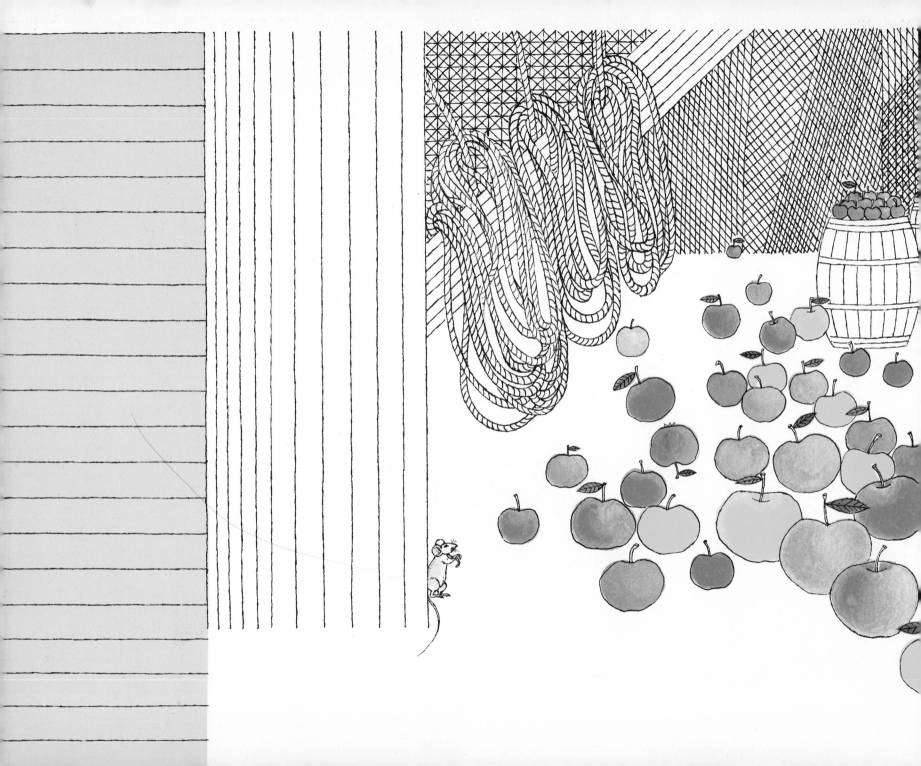

And apples in the hold,

The sails were made of silk,

And the masts were made of gold.

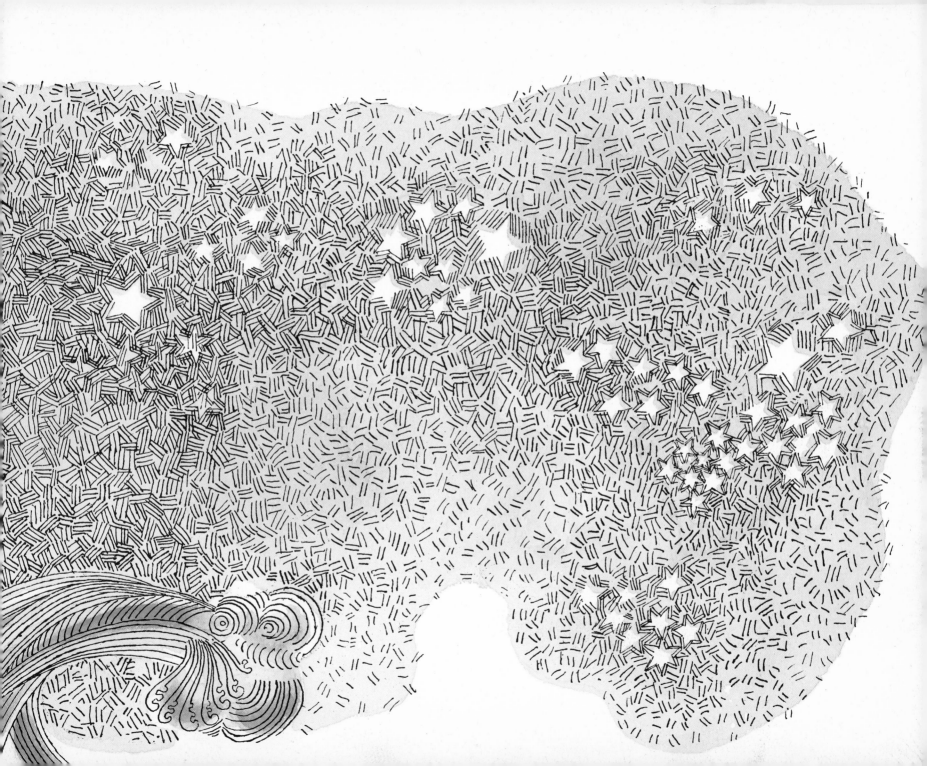

The four-and-twenty sailors

That stood upon the decks

Were four-and-twenty white mice,
With chains around their necks.
with gold necklaces

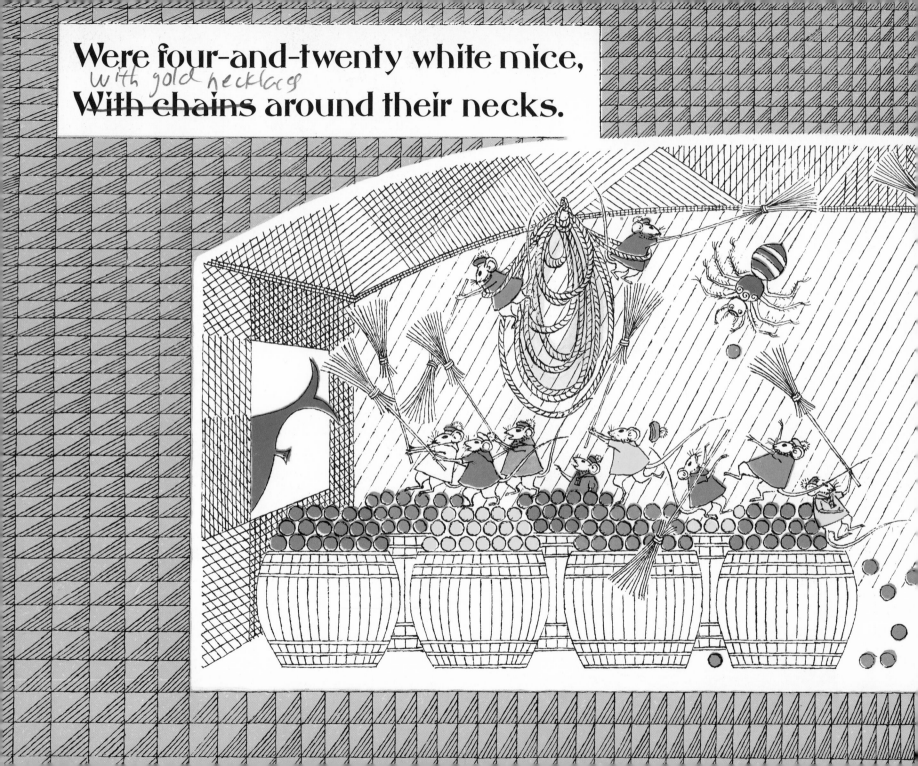

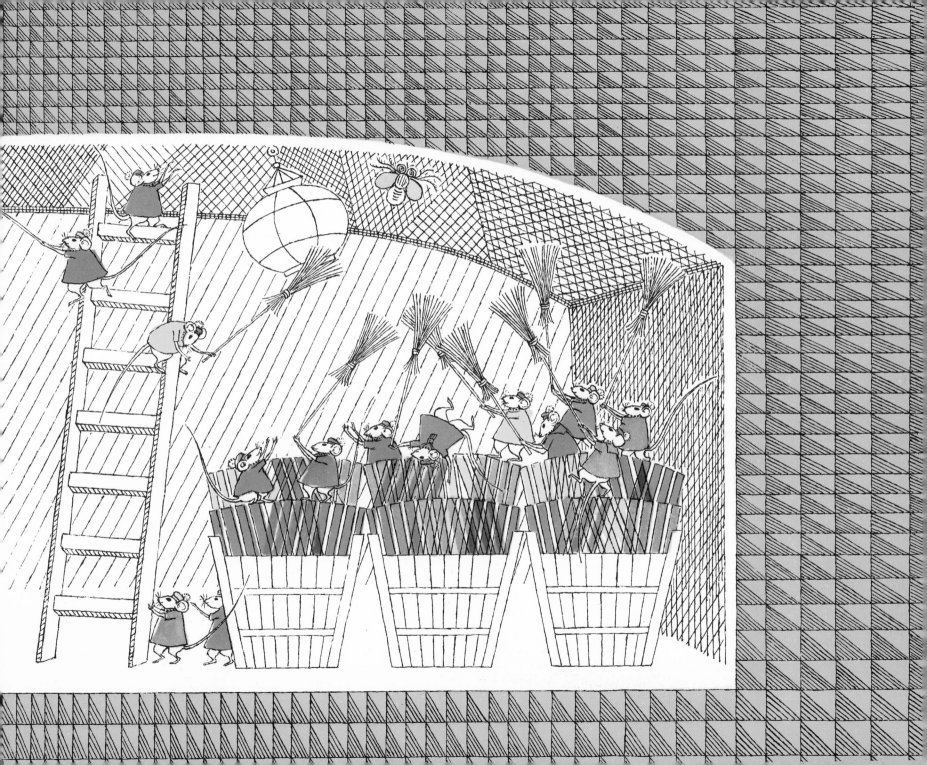

The captain was a duck,

With a packet on his back,

And when the ship began to move,

The captain cried,
"Quack, quack!"

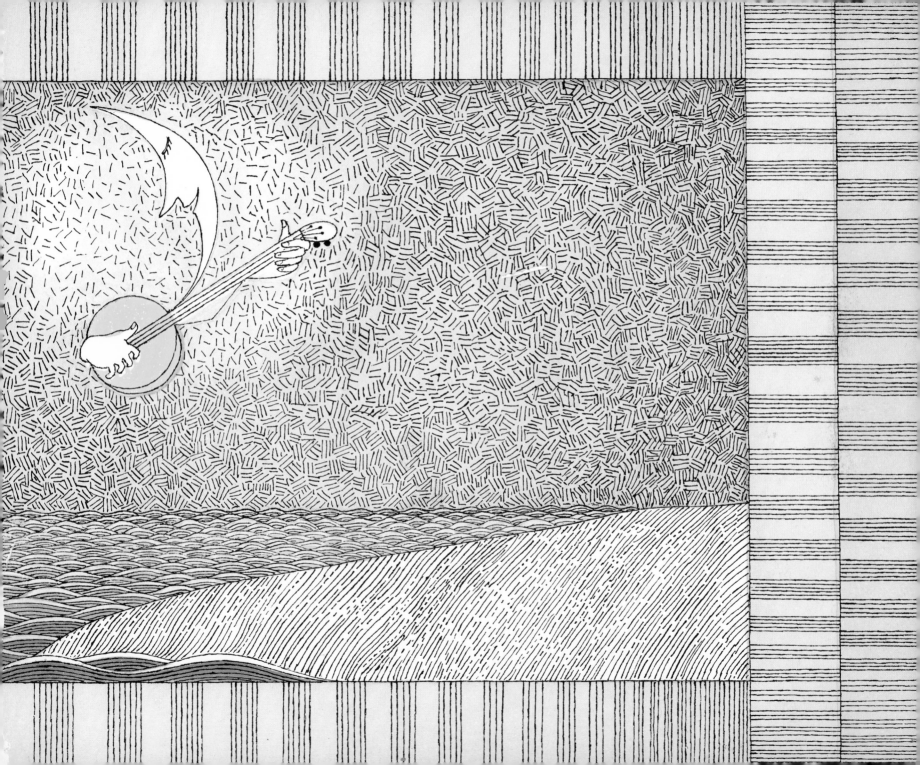